Riddles, Puzzles &
THINGS TO DO!

By Greg Jackson

Watermill Press

Contents

Travelin'

To find the hidden picture, start at number 1, and follow
the dots carefully.

Make Up A Story

Put together any combination of a #1, #2 and #3 picture, to make up any story you choose.

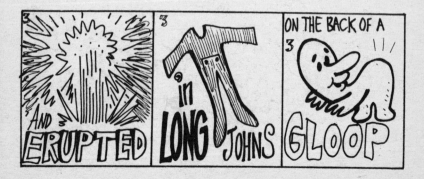

7

Shopping

Paul and Betty have come to the supermarket to do some shopping for their mother—but they wrote their list so fast that all the words are scrambled. Can you help them unscramble the list so they can do their shopping?

1. T E M A
2. O T O A E T P S
3. A D S O
4. C O B A N
5. P I S N C A H
6. I E C C M R E A
7. R D B E A
8. T U B R E T

1. _ _ _ _
2. _ _ _ _ _ _ _
3. _ _ _ _
4. _ _ _ _ _

5. _ _ _ _ _ _ _
6. _ _ _ _ _ _ _
7. _ _ _ _ _
8. _ _ _ _ _ _

Answer on page 62.

Down the Aisles

Playtime

Fit the name of each object pictured below into the boxes with the same numbers on the opposite page. **A** stands for Across, and **D** stands for Down.

Answer on page 62.

Paint With Tissue

Cut or tear pieces of as many different colors of tissue paper as you can find. Arrange the pieces on a piece of white board or construction paper. Brush lightly over your design with a wet paint brush or sponge, and remove the tissue pieces. The stains they leave behind will make a lovely painting.

Paint With Yarn

Think of a picture you'd like to "paint." Then cover a piece of cardboard with rubber cement, and while it is sticky, place your yarn on the board to form your picture. When you have finished arranging the yarn, just rub the cement away from where it isn't needed. Painting with yarn is fun and easy to do.

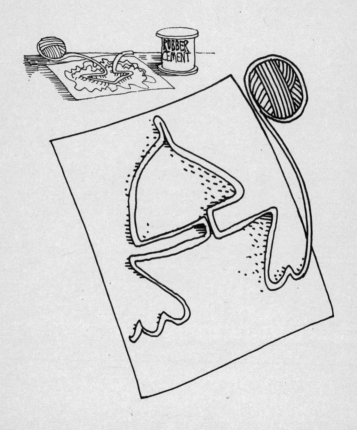

Pairing Up

Can you pair up the names of these objects to make the names of four *other* objects?

Answer on page 62.

Once A Year

Solve this rebus puzzle by adding and subtracting the letters in the names of the things pictured below. Follow the order shown by the plus and minus signs. When you have finished, your word should exactly fit the number of squares provided for the answer.

_ _ _ _ _ _

Color Mokihana of Hawaii

Color Nanook of Alaska

Around and Around

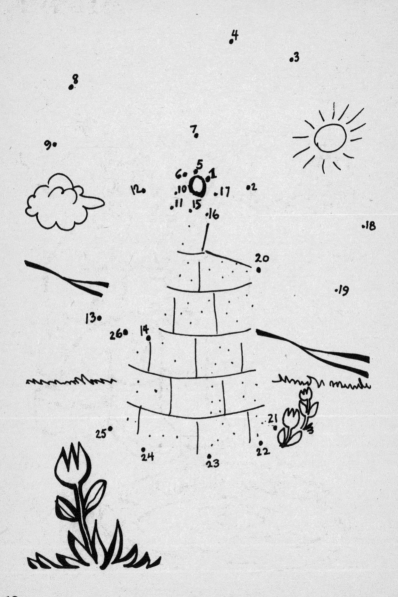

Laugh Time

1st Cowboy:
Say, Tex, how come you only wear one spur?

2nd Cowboy:
Well, Slim, I figure if one side of my horse gets going, the other side will come along, too.

Teacher: "If I gave you two apples, and told you to give one to your brother, would you give him the little one or the big one?"

Johnny: "It depends. Do you mean my *big* brother, or my *little* brother?"

Teacher: "Billy, why are you late for school?"

Billy: "Well, a sign down the street said . . ."

Teacher: "What can a *sign* have to do with it?"

Billy: "The sign said: School ahead, go slow."

19

At the Beach

For instructions, see page 10.

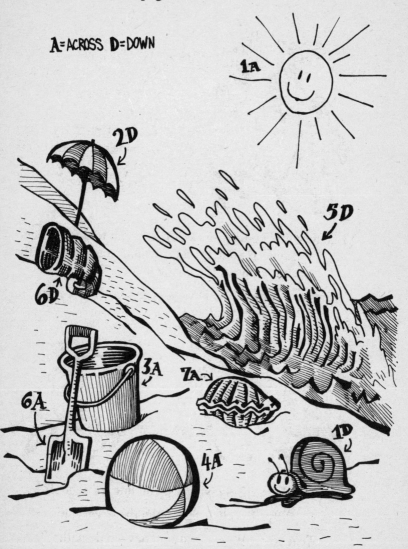

A=ACROSS D=DOWN

1A
2D
5D
6D
3A
7A
6A
1D
4A

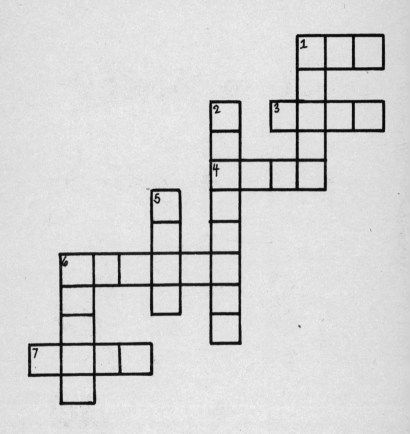

Answer on page 62.

Something Delicious

For instructions, see page 15.

Answer on page 62.

Making Music

Here are two musical instruments that are easy to make and fun to use — and they can be part of your own rhythm band when you've finished them!

TAMBOURINE: Put two aluminum pie plates together, as shown. Punch three pairs of holes in them and pull pretty ribbon through each hole. Before tying the ribbons, add a bell to each knot, so your tambourine will make music when you shake it.

MARACAS: Maracas are Latin-American musical instruments made from gourds filled with dried seeds. To make your own, use bottles like the ones shown, and paint bright designs on them. Then put dried beans or seeds in the bottles, and when you shake them in time to the music, they will make a nice sound.

A Maze-ing

José and Maria have just moved to town. Can you help them find their way to school?

Answer on page 62.

A Word Wheel

Complete this word wheel by filling in the name of each object under its picture. The last letter of each name is the first letter of the next name.

Answer on page 63.

Having a Party

Parties are fun — especially when you make the decorations and games for them yourself. Here are some party ideas for you and your friends:

PAPER LANTERNS: Fold a piece of white or colored paper in half the long way, and cut from the folded side almost to the edge (see Picture 1). Then open the paper up and paste the two end strips, as shown in Picture 2, to form the lantern. Hang your lanterns up with string drawn through two holes punched at the top.

NAME PENNANTS: Cut pennants from colored paper, and attach them to toothpicks. Write the name of a guest on each pennant, stick the toothpick into a gumdrop— and you have colorful place cards, showing your guests just where to sit.

CLOWN HATS: For each hat, cut a quarter-circle of colored paper, as shown in Pic. 1. Draw and color a design on each hat. Paste colored streamers to the points, and then roll each hat into a cone shape large enough to fit your head, and fasten the paper together (Pic. 2). Make enough hats for all your guests.

1

2

fasten

Silly Faces

You can have lots of fun making silly faces with these pictures. Start by cutting out or tracing each strip of pictures along the outside lines. Then paste the pictures to cardboard and cut them along the dotted lines. Now you can make new faces by switching the top, middle and bottom parts around. You and your friends can have a contest to see who can make the silliest face.

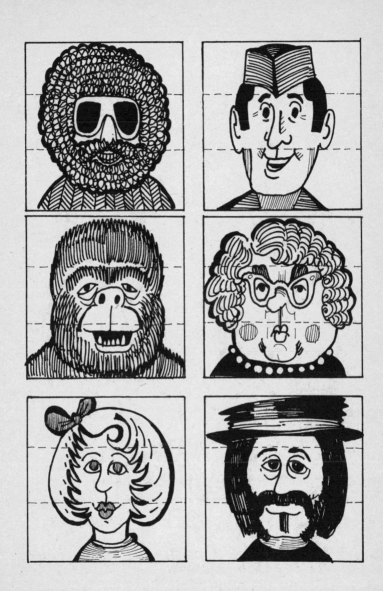

Animals All Around

For instructions, see page 10.

A = ACROSS D = DOWN

5D
9D
10A
7A
1D
6A
8D
2D
8A
3D
4D

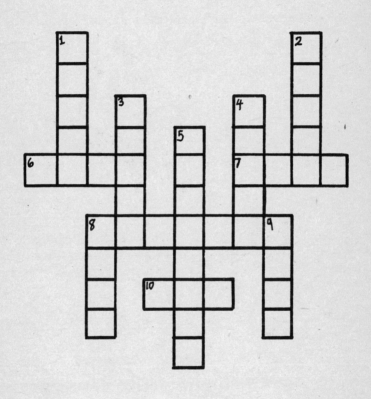

Answer on page 63.

Animal Jokes

Customer: When I bought this cat, you told me he was good for mice — but he doesn't go anywhere *near* them!

Pet Store Clerk: Well, isn't that good for mice?

Cowboy:
Well sir, did you find the horse well-behaved?

Dude:
I should say so! Whenever we came to a fence, he stopped and let me go over first!

Joe:
Why does your dog turn around so many times before he lies down?

Pete:
He's a watchdog, and he's winding himself up.

Henny: A snake snapped at me.

Penny: Snakes *strike* — they don't snap.

Henny: This one was a garter snake.

Riddles

What is the difference between a farmer and a dressmaker?
One gathers what he sows, the other sews what she gathers.

Name a carpenter's tool you can spell forward and backward the same way.
Level.

What is the biggest kind of ant?
A gi-ant.

When is it socially correct to serve milk in a saucer?
When you feed a cat.

Hidden Name

Find the name of a famous United States president by writing the first letter of each object in the square below its picture.

Answer on page 63.

At the Circus

There are 10 errors in this picture. How many can you find?

Big and Beautiful

For instructions, see page 15.

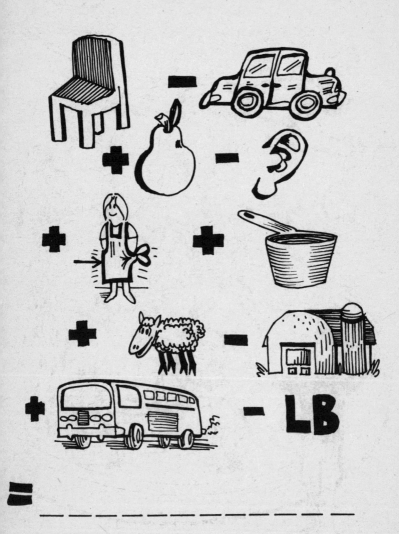

Answer on page 63.

Two and Two

Eight objects are shown below. If they are put together in the right pairs, they will combine to make the names of four *different* objects.

Answer on page 63.

Animal Mobile

This mobile is easy and fun to make. After you have finished the puzzles on pages 37 and 40, cut out the animals and paste them to a piece of cardboard. Color the pictures and cut them out. Then take some drinking straws (or straight sticks) and tie your pictures to them with thread, so they will look like they are floating in space.

In the Kitchen

For instructions, see page 10.

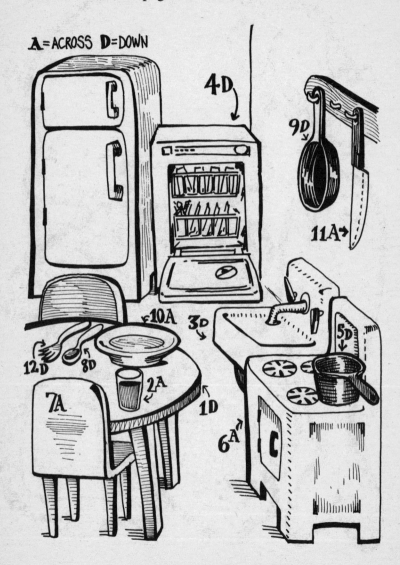

A=ACROSS D=DOWN

4D

9D

11A

10A

3D

12D

8D

2A

1D

7A

5D

6A

Answer on page 63.

Fat and Lean

Fill in the missing words in the nursery rhyme below, and then follow-the-dots on the opposite page to finish the picture that goes with the poem.

JACK SPRAT COULD EAT NO _____

HIS WIFE COULD EAT NO _____

AND SO BETWEEN THEM BOTH, YOU SEE,

THEY LICKED THE PLATTER _____

Puzzlers

What makes everyone sick except those who swallow it?
Flattery.

Why is a good resolution like a looking glass?
Because it is so easily broken.

What goes "Oom! Oom!"?
A cow walking backwards.

What did the baby sardine say when he saw a submarine?
Look! There goes a can of people!

What three keys won't open doors?
Monkeys, donkeys and turkeys.

What is a pig doing when he eats?
Making a hog of himself.

What is red, white and blue with red dots?
Uncle Sam with the measles.

How Many C's?

There are 13 things in this picture whose names start with the letter C. How many can you find?

Answer on page 63.

Chuckles

City Slicker: I just bought a farm ten miles (16 km)
long and one inch (2½ cm) wide.

Farmer: That so? What are you going to raise on it?

City Slicker: Spaghetti.

First Cannibal: I don't like your friend.

Second Cannibal: O.K., just eat the vegetables.

Teacher: How did this window get broken?

Billy: I was cleaning my slingshot, and it went off.

Billy: I've lost my dog.

Silly: Why don't you put an ad in the paper?

Billy: What for? My dog can't read!

Sally: (Crying bitterly) "My new shoes are hurting
me!"

Teacher: "Well, no wonder, you have them on the wrong
feet!"

Sally: (Crying even more) "But I haven't *got* any
other feet!"

Moon Walk

Answer on page 64.

Find the Twins

In each row, there are only two pictures that are *exactly* the same. Can you find them?

Answer on page 64.

Hidden Words

How many words can you make from the letters in the word

APARTMENT

_____   _____   _____
_____   _____   _____
_____   _____   _____
_____   _____   _____
_____   _____   _____
_____   _____   _____
_____   _____   _____
_____   _____   _____
_____   _____   _____
_____   _____   _____
_____   _____   _____
_____   _____   _____
_____   _____   _____
_____   _____   _____
_____   _____   _____
_____   _____   _____

In the Schoolroom

For instructions, see page 10.

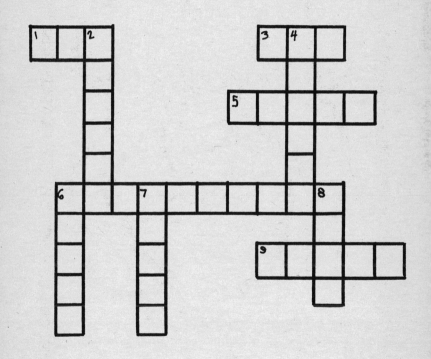

Answer on page 64.

A Jig-Saw Puzzle

Trace this picture and then color it and glue it to a piece of cardboard. When the glue is dry, cut the picture along the dotted lines and you will have a jigsaw puzzle.

More Riddles

What is it one frequently holds but rarely touches?
His tongue.

What side of an apple is the left side?
The side that hasn't been eaten yet.

Why do birds fly south?
Because it's too far to walk.

Why are different trees like different dogs?
Because each has a different bark.

What divides by uniting?
Scissors.

What kinds of animals can jump higher than a house?
All kinds of animals — houses can't jump.

Hidden Carrots

Freddy Bunny hid nine carrots for the winter, but he hid them so well that now he can only find one of them. Can you help him find the other eight carrots?

A Coloring Puzzle

There is a picture hidden in the spaces below. To find it, color in the spaces with the right color for each space.

1. RED   2. BLUE   3. YELLOW   4. PINK

A Hidden Picture

To find the hidden picture, copy the details from each box on this page into the proper boxes on the opposite page.

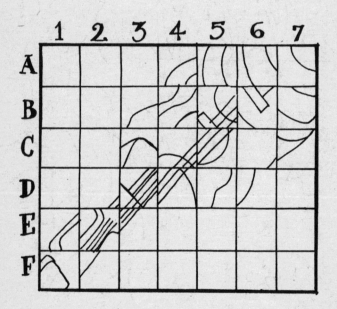

	A	B	C	D	E	F
1						
2						
3						
4						
5						
6						
7						

Playing

For instructions, see page 15.

Answer on page 64.

Happy Birthday

Timmy likes all his birthday presents, but there's one he can't put together by himself. Can you help him? To find the hidden picture, start at Number 1 and follow the dots carefully.

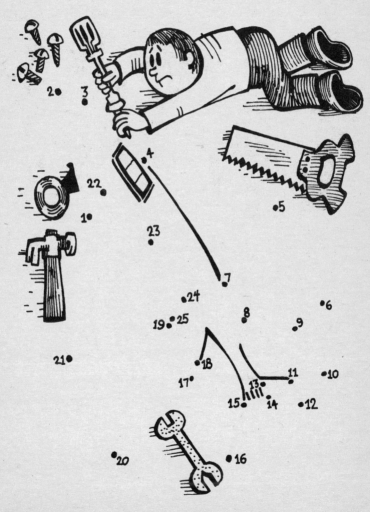

On the Farm

For instructions, see page 10.

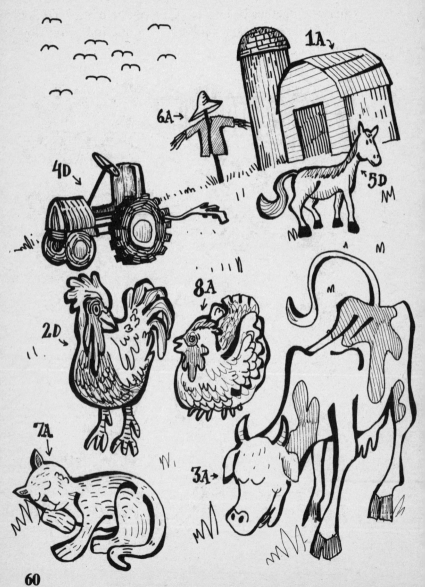

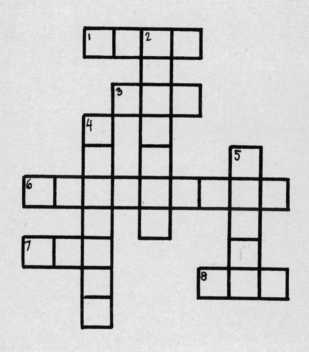

Answer on page 64.

Answers

page 8

1. meat; 2. potatoes; 3. soda; 4. bacon; 5. spinach; 6. ice cream; 7. bread; 8. butter.

page 10

page 14

cat + fish = catfish; match + box = matchbox; tree + house = tree house; cup + cake = cupcake.

page 15

bird + log + pot − dog + hand + ear − plane − oar + daisy − DIS = BIRTHDAY.

page 20

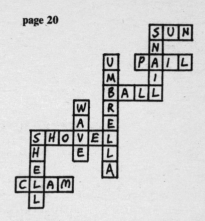

page 22

hat + mower − tower + bone + cup − cone + cart − P − cat + finger − fin = HAMBURGER.

page 24

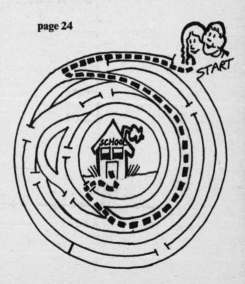

page 25

trunk, knife, earth, hands, sheep, pilot.

page 30

page 34

A(pple) + D(rum) + A(lligator) + M(onkey) + S(quirrel) = ADAMS

page 36

chair — car + pear — ear + apron + pot + lamb — barn + bus — LB = HIPPOPOTAMUS

page 37

box + car = boxcar
shoe + tree = shoe tree
star + fish = starfish
bird + house = birdhouse

page 40

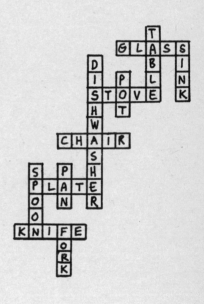

page 45

ceiling, clock, cloud, chimney, car, curtains, coat, cushion, chair, candle, cat, can, carpet.

Answers

page 47

page 50

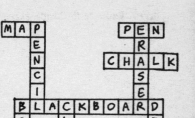

page 58

plate + boy + dog − boot + rock − deck + tug + piano − goat + bed − pie − B = **PLAYGROUND**

page 60

page 48

Cups: #3 and #6
Pictures: #1 and #5
Dogs: #1 and #6